BASIC / NOT BORING
SCIENCE SKILLS

SCIENCE CONCEPTS & PROCESSES

Grades 6–8⁺

Inventive Exercises to Sharpen
Skills and Raise Achievement

Series Concept & Development
by Imogene Forte & Marjorie Frank
Exercises by Marjorie Frank

Incentive Publications, Inc.
Nashville, Tennessee

About the cover:
Bound resist, or tie dye, is the most ancient known method of fabric surface design. The brilliance of the basic tie dye design on this cover reflects the possibilities that emerge from the mastery of basic skills.

Illustrated by Kathleen Bullock
Cover art by Mary Patricia Deprez, dba Tye Dye Mary®
Cover design by Marta Drayton, Joe Shibley, and W. Paul Nance
Edited by Jean K. Signor

ISBN 0-86530-553-6

PRINTED IN THE UNITED STATES OF AMERICA
www.incentivepublications.com

TABLE OF CONTENTS

CELEBRATE BASIC SCIENCE SKILLS

Basic does not mean boring! There is certainly nothing dull about. . .
   . . . searching for science in a backpack, on a roller coaster, or at a rock concert
   . . . snooping around to solve mysteries involving atom bombs, chromosomes, pyramids
      and quasars
   . . . knowing how to tell an orinthologist from an ichthyologist
   . . . exploring the wonders of inventions like DVDs, EKGs, fax machines, and inner tubes
   . . . tracking down the difference between the Chaos Theory and the Quark Theory
   . . . showing off that you know how life is affected by a GPS or an aqualung
   . . . fooling around with singing glasses, tongue maps, falling eggs, and swinging forks
   . . . deciding what's harmful about electric scooters, credit cards, and the Internet

These are just some of the adventures students can explore as they celebrate basic science skills. The idea of celebrating the basics is just what it sounds like-enjoying and getting good at knowing all about the big ideas of science and the processes scientists use to understand the natural world. Each page invites learners to try a high-interest, appealing exercise that will sharpen or review one specific science skill, concept, or process. This is no ordinary fill-in-the-blanks way to learn! These exercises are fun and surprising. Students will do the useful work of deepening science knowledge while they enjoy five clever scientists who lead them to explore and deepen their understanding of science concepts and processes.

The pages in this book can be used in many ways:
   • to sharpen or review a skill with one student
   • to reinforce the skill with a small or large group
   • by students working on their own
   • by students working under the direction of a parent or teacher

Each page may be used to introduce a new skill, to reinforce a skill, or to assess a student's performance or understanding. And there's more here than just the great student activity pages. You'll also find an appendix of resources helpful to students and teachers—including a ready-to-use test for assessing science concepts and process skills.

The pages are written with the assumption that an adult will be available to assist the student with his or her learning and practice. It will be helpful for students to have access to science resources such as a science textbook, encyclopedias, and Internet reference sources.

As your students take on the challenges of these adventures with science concepts and processes, they will grow. As you watch them check off the basic science skills they have sharpened, you can celebrate with them!

The Skills Test (pages 56–59)
   Use the skills test as a pretest and/or a post-test. This will help you check the students' mastery of basic skills and understandings in the area of science concepts and processes. It can also prepare them for success on tests of standards, instructional goals, or other individual achievement.

SCIENCE CONCEPTS & PROCESSES SKILLS CHECKLIST

✔	SKILL	PAGE(S)
	Show understanding of the nature of scientific research and discoveries	10–11
	Show understanding of science as a human endeavor	10–11
	Show understanding of the limitations of science	10–11, 22–23
	Distinguish among different branches of science; Identify the topics and areas associated with different branches of science	11, 12–13
	Identify some important scientific discoveries and inventions	14–17
	Recognize the significance of important scientific discoveries and inventions	14–17
	Identify some key events in the history of science	14–17, 18–19
	Show recognition of the relationship between science and the personal and social realms; identify ways science impacts personal life	20–21
	Identify some uses of science and technology	22–23
	Show understandings of the relationship between science and technology	22–23
	Show understanding of the benefits and consequences to society of science and technology	23
	Recognize some key scientific theories and laws	24–25
	Show understanding of the nature and method of scientific inquiry	26–27
	Recognize and distinguish between key concepts in science	28–29
	Show understanding of the concept of systems	30
	Show understanding of the concepts of order and organization	31
	Show understanding of the concept of structure and function; explain how structure and function are related in specific instances	32–33
	Show understanding of the concept of the energy-matter relationship	34
	Show understanding of the concept of cause and effect	35
	Show understanding of the concepts of change	36
	Show understanding of the concept of constancy	36
	Show understanding of the concept of equilibrium	37
	Show understanding of the concept of evolution	37
	Show understanding of the concept of cycle; identify stages in various kinds of cycles	38
	Relate the big ideas of science (the concepts) to life situations	39
	Understand and use the process of observation	40–41
	Understand and use the process of classification	42–43
	Understand and use the process of forming a hypothesis	44–45
	Understand and use the processes of measurement and using numbers	46
	Understand and use the processes of interpreting data and predicting outcomes	47
	Understand and use the process of using models	48
	Understand and use the processes of communicating results	49
	Understand and use the process of designing an experiment (including identifying and controlling variables)	50–51
	Recognize some safety procedures for science experimentation	52

SCIENCE
CONCEPTS & PROCESSES
Skills Exercises

SCIENCE STATEMENTS UNDER SCRUTINY

The brilliant physicist, Dr. R. R. Radon, knows plenty about science. So, his scientific statements are generally accurate. Scrutinize each group of statements. In each group, identify the statement or statements that he would make (assuming he's making true statements). Circle the correct letter or letters.

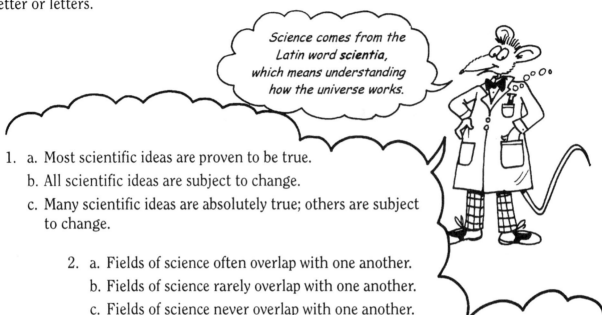

Science comes from the Latin word scientia, which means understanding how the universe works.

1. a. Most scientific ideas are proven to be true.
   b. All scientific ideas are subject to change.
   c. Many scientific ideas are absolutely true; others are subject to change.

2. a. Fields of science often overlap with one another.
   b. Fields of science rarely overlap with one another.
   c. Fields of science never overlap with one another.

3. a. Most scientists have the same set of skills and abilities.
   b. Scientists have a wide range of different interests, skills, and abilities.
   c. All scientists in one field of study share the same skills and abilities.

4. a. Science did not exist until after the Middle Ages.
   b. The first scientific discovery was the discovery that the Earth is round.
   c. Scientific discoveries began thousands of years ago, probably as early as human life began.

5. a. Important contributions to science have been made by men and women of many different cultures, countries, and ethnic backgrounds, over a long period of time.
   b. Most important scientific discoveries have been made by men in the Western Hemisphere.
   c. Most important scientific discoveries have been made in the last one hundred years.

6. a. When different scientists investigate the same problem, they keep working until they all agree on the results of their studies before they publish the results.
   b. Scientists researching the same problem often find and publish different results.
   c. Scientists researching the same problem usually publish similar results.

Use with page 11.

Name _____

7. a. Good scientific research requires the use of human qualities such as curiosity, creativity, honesty, and judgment.
   b. Good scientific research requires that scientists disregard personal beliefs and ethics.
   c. Good scientific research requires that scientists start with a brand new idea or question that has not been considered before.

8. a. Eventually, science will probably be able to solve all human problems.
   b. Eventually, science will probably be able to solve most human problems.
   c. There will continue to be human problems that science cannot solve.

9. a. Scientific explanations place heavy importance on evidence.
   b. Most scientific explanations or conclusions also raise more questions.
   c. Math is important to all aspects of scientific discovery

10. a. Most scientists work alone.
    b. Most scientists work in teams.
    c. All scientists work in laboratories

Professor Radon's poster shows the main branches of science. Look at the fields of scientific study shown below. For each field, identify the branch to which it belongs.
(Write **L, E & S, P, M,** or **Soc** for each field.)

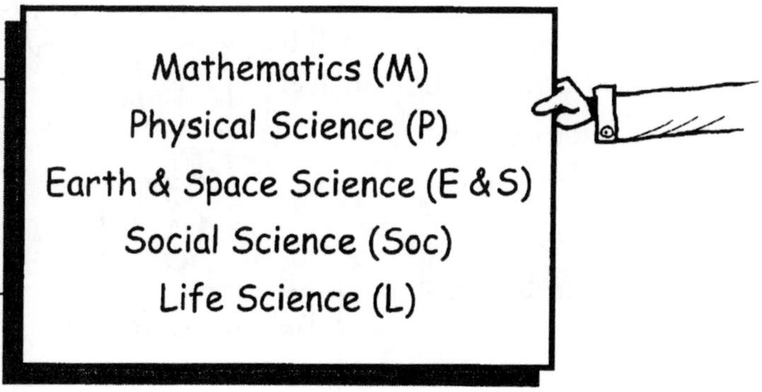

Mathematics (M)
Physical Science (P)
Earth & Space Science (E & S)
Social Science (Soc)
Life Science (L)

_____ 11. seismology

_____ 12. genetics

_____ 13. psychology

_____ 14. chemistry

_____ 15. aeronautics

_____ 16. biology

_____ 17. statistics

_____ 18. meteorology

_____ 19. zoology

_____ 20. anthropology

_____ 21. geometry

_____ 22. economics

_____ 23. astronomy

_____ 24. anatomy

Use with page 10.

Name

WHO STUDIES WHAT?

There are dozens of different kinds of scientists, all asking dozens of questions about the way the world works. If you follow a scientist around for a while, you would notice what kinds of things she or he studies. Here are just a few of the things scientists study. Which scientist from which field of study would study which topic? Choose the best answer for each area of study on this page and page 13.

Which scientist would study . . .

1. stars and planets?
   a. an anatomist
   b. an electrician
   c. an astronomer
   d. a physician

2. prehistoric forms of life?
   a. a paleontologist
   b. a mechanical engineer
   c. a hydrologist
   d. a political scientist

3. living organisms too small to be seen with the human eye?
   a. a microeconomist
   b. a psychologist
   c. a sociologist
   d. a microbiologist

4. birds?
   a. an entomologist
   b. a botanist
   c. an embryologist
   d. an ornithologist

5. rocks?
   a. an astronomer
   b. a petrologist
   c. a hematologist
   d. a rheumatologist

Dr. R.R. Radon,
a. _____

Dr. Felicia Femur,
b. _____

Prof. Agnes Igneous,
c. _____

6. ways the body can be protected against disease?
   a. a metallurgist
   b. an immunologist
   c. an ophthalmologist
   d. an ecologist

7. soil and crop-raising?
   a. a psychiatrist
   b. an aeronautic engineer
   c. an agronomist
   d. an anatomist

8. structure of matter?
   a. a statistician
   b. a political scientist
   c. a chemist
   d. a cytologist

9. behavior of human groups?
   a. a sociologist
   b. a civil engineer
   c. a physicist
   d. an organic chemist

10. development of language?
    a. an oncologist
    b. a morphologist
    c. a linguist
    d. a hematologist

11. tides and waves?
    a. an oceanographer
    b. a mineralogist
    c. a microeconomist
    d. a geologist

Use with page 13.

Name

12. financial systems?
    a. an economist
    b. an ecologist
    c. a taxonomist
    d. a cryogenist

Ozzie Moses,
d. _____

13. past cultures?
    a. an archaeologist
    b. an agronomist
    c. an histologist
    d. a radiologist

Lester
Asteroid
e. _____

14. human DNA?
    a. an oceanographer
    b. a geographer
    c. a geneticist
    d. an astrophysicist

15. fission and fusion
    of atoms?
    a. a neurologist
    b. a nuclear physicist
    c. a physiologist
    d. a cartographer

16. weather?
    a. an organic chemist
    b. a pathologist
    c. a biologist
    d. a meteorologist

17. energy and force?
    a. a dermatologist
    b. a bacteriologist
    c. a mathematician
    d. a physicist

18. insects?
    a. an entomologist
    b. an etymologist
    c. a paleontologist
    d. an histologist

19. human behavior?
    a. a physiologist
    b. a molecular
       biologist
    c. a psychologist
    d. a petrologist

20. pollution?
    a. a psychiatrist
    b. an ecologist
    c. an anthropologist
    d. an embryologist

21. matter at very low temperatures?
    a. an anatomist
    b. a linguist
    c. a cryogenist
    d. an orthodontist

22. human cultures?
    a. an anthropologist
    b. a biochemist
    c. a neurologist
    d. a bacteriologist

23. behavior and properties
    of cells?
    a. a geologist
    b. a meteorologist
    c. a taxonomist
    d. a cytologist

24. logic?
    a. a mathematician
    b. a biophysicist
    c. a climatologist
    d. a geneticist

25. plants?
    a. a zoologist
    b. a botanist
    c. an ornithologist
    d. a criminologist

26. human body systems?
    a. an ichthyologist
    b. a quantum mechanic
    c. a seismologist
    d. a physiologist

27. Look at the professors pictured on these two pages.
    Make a careful guess about what kind of scientist each
    one might be. Write your guess beside each one.

Use with page 12.

Name

DAZZLING DISCOVERIES & INGENIOUS INVENTIONS

Wow! Look at the ideas pouring out of the "Good Idea" Machine.

Match each description with a discovery or invention. Write the correct letter on the line.
(Use the descriptions and inventions on both pages--14 and 15.)

DING

A. anesthetics
B. antibiotics
C. antiseptics
D. atom
E. cathode ray tube
F. combustion
G. DVD
H. ECG
I. electric light bulb
J. electricity
K. electromagnetic power
L. fax machine

Thousands of inventions and discoveries fill the science books and journals. Here are a few of the most dazzling, awesome, life-changing, ingenious, or memorable.

____ 1. Dr. Alexander Fleming's 1920 discovery revolutionized medicine and treated millions of people with serious diseases.

____ 2. In 1910, French chemist, George Claude, ran electricity through a tube of gas and produced a colored light that led to the "lighting up" of advertising signs.

____ 3. In the 1777, French scientist Antoine Lavoisier made a discovery about oxygen's role in the burning of matter.

____ 4. In 1803, English Chemist, John Dalton, came up with the idea that matter consists of small, indivisible particles.

____ 5. An invention of the late 20th century gave TV and computer viewers ways to listen to richer sounds and watch cleaner pictures than were ever available before.

____ 6. In the mid-1900s, Johannes Gutenberg invented a machine for publishing books quickly.

____ 7. Samuel Morse's 1838 invention sent long-distance messages over a wire using bursts of electricity to make sounds.

____ 8. In 1898, Marie and Pierre Curie discovered an element that made the development of atomic energy possible.

____ 9. In 1831, Michael Faraday discovered a new way to produce electricity, which made it possible to build electric generators.

____ 10. After German scientist Wilhelm Konrad von Rontgen made this 1895 discovery by accident, doctors had a new look inside bodies.

____ 11. Roger Bacon's discoveries in the late 1200s led to better eyesight for centuries to follow.

____ 12. A 1543 Copernicus discovery led to greater understanding of the universe.

Use with page 15.

Name

___ 13. As early as 3000 B.C., The Egyptians used this system to make measurements they needed to build the pyramids.

___ 14. Vladimir Zworykin's work in the 1930s led to the invention that made the first televisions possible.

___ 15. A 1904 invention by German physicist Arthur Korn allows someone to send writing and pictures across a telephone line.

___ 16. This 1901 invention by Dutch scientist Willem Einthoven allowed hospitals to check the heartbeats and look for signs of heart disease in patients

___ 17. British surgeon, Joseph Lister's discovery in the 1800s reduced the chances of infection developing in the wounds created by surgery.

___ 18. In the mid 1500s, Gerardus Mercator found a way to represent distances on the Earth's surface onto pieces of paper.

___ 19. Galileo Galilei's invention allowed him to see the surface of the moon in the early 1600s.

___ 20. When Alexander Graham Bell invented the machine that allowed him to talk to someone far away in 1876, he probably never dreamed of e-mail or fax machines.

___ 21. Charles Goodyear found a way to make tires softer by putting air inside them.

M. geometry

N. gravity

O. helicopter

P. Heliocentric Theory

Q. inner tube

R. jet engine

S. genome project

T. lenses

U. logic

V. maps

W. X-rays

X. microscope

Y. neon lights

Z. printing press

AA. radium

BB. telegraph

CC. telephone

DD. telescope

___ 22. Benjamin Franklin discovered this while flying a kite in a thunderstorm in 1752.

___ 23. Robert Hooke's tube for viewing very tiny objects was invented in the 1600s.

___ 24. With this 1930 invention, Sir Frank Whittle increased the speed of air travel.

___ 25. This invention, created by Sir Joseph Swan and Thomas Edison in the 1870s, gave light to rooms without burning out quickly.

___ 26. At the beginning of the 21st century, scientists developed the first maps of human genes.

___ 27. During the 300s B.C., Aristotle developed a system of reasoning for reaching conclusions.

___ 28. Igor Sikorsky developed the first flying machine that was able to take off and land vertically.

___ 29. As the story goes, a falling apple led to this Isaac Newton discovery in 1687.

___ 30. Surgery was a terribly painful process until 1846, when William Morton, an American dentist, discovered a way to put patients to sleep to overcome the pain.

What a great list !

Use with page 14.

Name

WHAT DIFFERENCE DOES IT MAKE?

Professor Felicia Femur is ecstatic about her new microscope. It helps her see and study cells more clearly than she has ever seen them before. Every scientific discovery has made some sort of difference in the world, and in the lives of the humans and other living things on Earth.

Tell what difference these have made. Describe at least one change that has been made possible or caused by **15 or more** of these scientific discoveries or inventions.

Ah ha!

Discoveries

radio waves_____

microwaves_____

fire_____

antibodies_____

solar-power_____

magnetic power_____

DNA_____

atomic power_____

salt_____

healing powers of the body_____

cells_____

antibiotics_____

Use with page 17.

Name

Inventions

I'm always looking for new inventions to help the world. Follow your own ideas! Invent something that will make a difference in the world. Draw your invention and explain it!
(Use posterboard.)

mortar_____

rubber_____

the wheel_____

lycra_____

microchips_____

the DVD_____

geometry_____

GPS_____

the LCD_____

e-mail_____

the sun dial_____

the transistor radio_____

disposable syringes_____

virtual reality_____

the jet engine _____

the aqualung_____

the Polaroid camera_____

the electric iron_____

the Hubble Space telescope_____

Use with page 16.

Name

HISTORY MYSTERIES

Scientists spend a lot of time tracking down unanswered questions and mysterious events. Do your own research to find out about some past happenings in science.

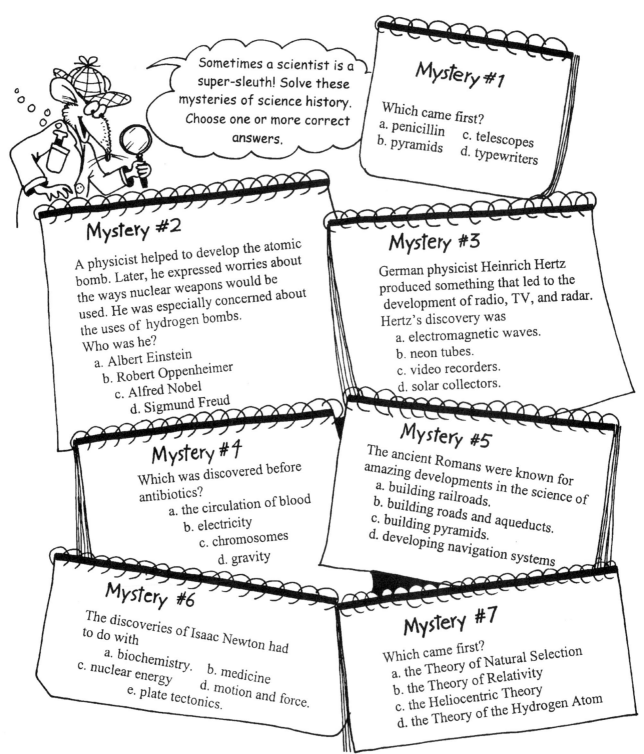

Sometimes a scientist is a super-sleuth! Solve these mysteries of science history. Choose one or more correct answers.

Mystery #1

Which came first?
a. penicillin
b. pyramids
c. telescopes
d. typewriters

Mystery #2

A physicist helped to develop the atomic bomb. Later, he expressed worries about the ways nuclear weapons would be used. He was especially concerned about the uses of hydrogen bombs. Who was he?
a. Albert Einstein
b. Robert Oppenheimer
c. Alfred Nobel
d. Sigmund Freud

Mystery #3

German physicist Heinrich Hertz produced something that led to the development of radio, TV, and radar. Hertz's discovery was
a. electromagnetic waves.
b. neon tubes.
c. video recorders.
d. solar collectors.

Mystery #4

Which was discovered before antibiotics?
a. the circulation of blood
b. electricity
c. chromosomes
d. gravity

Mystery #5

The ancient Romans were known for amazing developments in the science of
a. building railroads.
b. building roads and aqueducts.
c. building pyramids.
d. developing navigation systems

Mystery #6

The discoveries of Isaac Newton had to do with
a. biochemistry.
b. medicine
c. nuclear energy
d. motion and force.
e. plate tectonics.

Mystery #7

Which came first?
a. the Theory of Natural Selection
b. the Theory of Relativity
c. the Heliocentric Theory
d. the Theory of the Hydrogen Atom

Use with page 19.

Name

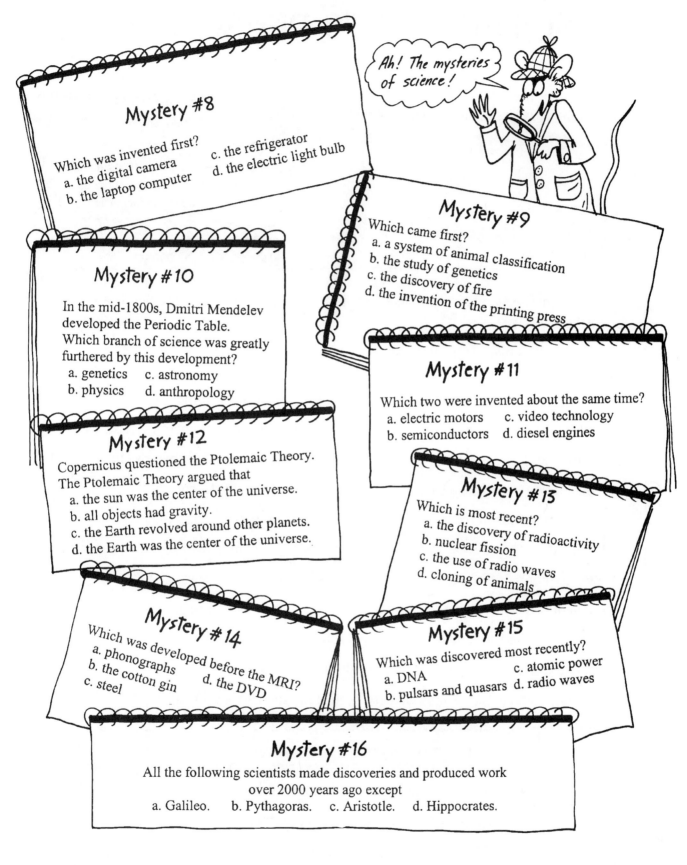

Ah! The mysteries of science!

Mystery #8

Which was invented first?
a. the digital camera
b. the laptop computer
c. the refrigerator
d. the electric light bulb

Mystery #9

Which came first?
a. a system of animal classification
b. the study of genetics
c. the discovery of fire
d. the invention of the printing press

Mystery #10

In the mid-1800s, Dmitri Mendelev developed the Periodic Table. Which branch of science was greatly furthered by this development?
a. genetics   c. astronomy
b. physics   d. anthropology

Mystery #11

Which two were invented about the same time?
a. electric motors   c. video technology
b. semiconductors   d. diesel engines

Mystery #12

Copernicus questioned the Ptolemaic Theory. The Ptolemaic Theory argued that
a. the sun was the center of the universe.
b. all objects had gravity.
c. the Earth revolved around other planets.
d. the Earth was the center of the universe.

Mystery #13

Which is most recent?
a. the discovery of radioactivity
b. nuclear fission
c. the use of radio waves
d. cloning of animals

Mystery #14

Which was developed before the MRI?
a. phonographs
b. the cotton gin   d. the DVD
c. steel

Mystery #15

Which was discovered most recently?
a. DNA   c. atomic power
b. pulsars and quasars d. radio waves

Mystery #16

All the following scientists made discoveries and produced work over 2000 years ago except
a. Galileo.   b. Pythagoras.   c. Aristotle.   d. Hippocrates.

Use with page 18.

Name

SCIENCE GETS PERSONAL

Professor Ozzie Moses is getting ready for a discussion with his students. They will talk about how science affects their personal lives. Unfortunately, his typist made many errors in the notes for his class. Something is wrong in almost every or every item on his notes.

> If you find a correct item, circle its number. For the other items, make changes to correct the wrong information.

1. Individual humans can have no effect on the ecological or health problems of a whole society.

2. Natural hazards, such as earthquakes and storms, can be eliminated with the help of science.

3. Technology has very few risks or negative consequences for human life and health.

4. There is no way to reduce the risks of harm from biological or chemical hazards.

5. With enough research, time, and money, science can meet all human needs.

6. Scientific research in a society is not affected by politics of the society.

7. There is no way to reduce the risks of damages from natural hazards.

8. Hazards in the natural world cannot be caused by human activities.

9. Prescription drugs only have healing effects on the human body.

10. Inventions of all kinds bring more benefits than hazards to humans.

11. Eventually science and technology will solve all human problems.

12. All natural substances are safe and healthy for the human body.

13. Regular exercise is the only element needed for good physical fitness

Choose one of the items above and give a full explanation of your answer.
Relate it to your own life experience.

14. Science can protect people from all natural disasters.

15. Scientists can freely do research on human subjects.

16. Use of tobacco products has no connection to illness.

Name

SURROUNDED BY SCIENCE

It's everywhere! In today's world, scientific discoveries and inventions affect every corner of our lives.

Describe at least one way that science is present in each of these places.

1. in a backpack

2. a downhill ski race

3. a roller coaster

4. a soccer game

5. a rock concert

6. ice cream shop

7. a city street

8. a school cafeteria

9. your bedroom

10. a subway

ICE CREAM SHOP

SUBWAY

Name

A TIGHT RELATIONSHIP

What do noisy jet engines, dry desert, splitting atoms, and black holes have in common? They are all connected to the needs and curiosities of humans and the technologies that develop from their scientific activities. Human society, science, and technology have a close relationship.

Put your scientific mind to work and answer these questions about science and technology and the way they work together in human society.

1. Which statements are accurate? *(Circle one or more.)*

    A. Science proposes answers for things happening in the natural world.
    B. Technology proposes solutions for human needs.
    C. Scientific study has consequences. The development of new technology does not.
    D. Science explores questions that require instruments or tools to answer.
    E. Scientists may identify problems that a technological tool can solve.
    F. New technology may cause problems that scientists must try to remedy.

Write another example for each of these.

2. Needs of society lead to the development of technology.

Example: The need for water to grow crops in dry land led to the development of irrigation systems.

Another Example: _____

3. Scientific discovery leads to technological developments.

Example: The discovery that the splitting of atoms gave off a tremendous amount of energy led to the development of nuclear power plants.

Another Example: _____

4. A technological tool can lead to scientific discovery.

Example: The invention of powerful telescopes made possible the discovery of black holes.

Another Example: _____

5. A technological development can create a societal need.

Example: The development of jet engines created issues of noise pollution and safety in cities.

Another Example: _____

Use with page 23.

Name

NO ESCAPE FROM CONSEQUENCES

Ingenious inventions and tricks of technology surround us. Every day, more awesome tools and toys are produced through scientific processes. We love the benefits of these tools and toys brought to us by the world's inventors, but every invention comes with costs or consequences of some kind.

DVD PLAYERS

Benefit_____

_____

Consequence_____

_____

AIRPORTS NEAR CITIES

Benefit_____

_____

Consequence_____

_____

ELECTRIC SCOOTERS

Benefit_____

_____

Consequence_____

_____

AUTOMATED FACTORIES

Benefit_____

_____

Consequence_____

_____

CREDIT CARDS

Benefit_____

_____

Consequence_____

_____

The INTERNET

Benefit_____

_____

Consequence_____

_____

Ponder each of these wonders of technology.
Then describe a benefit and a consequence or hazard of each.

Use with page 22.

Name _____

FANTASTIC EXPLANATIONS

Scientists come up with explanations for happenings they observe or discover. Those explanations often are stated in the form of theories or laws. Someone has started a file of some scientific laws and theories. Finish the file by writing a brief statement or summary of the theory named on each card. (Continue with the laws on page 25.)

A **scientific theory** is an explanation based on many observations during repeated experiments.

1.
Big Bang Theory

2.
Cell Theory

3.
Chaos Theory

4.
Continental Drift Theory

THEORIES B-C

5.
Electromagnetic Theory

6.
Theory of Evolution

7.
Germ Theory

8.
Heliocentric Theory

THEORIES D-O

9.
Plate Tectonics Theory

10.
Theory of Relativity

11.
Quark Theory

12.
String Theory

13.
Theory of Superconductivity

THEORIES P-Z

Use with page 25.

Name

On each card, write a brief statement or summary of the law named.

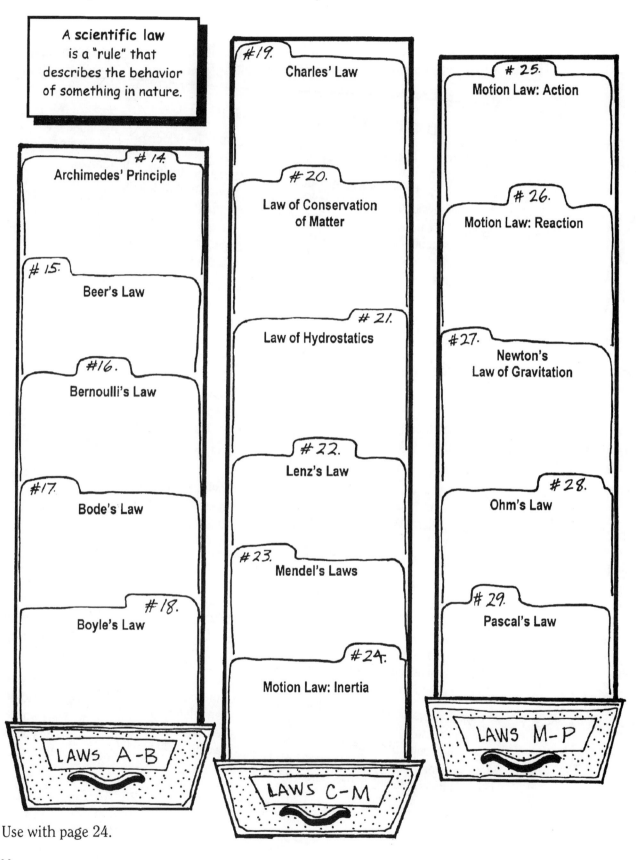

A **scientific law** is a "rule" that describes the behavior of something in nature.

#14. Archimedes' Principle

#15. Beer's Law

#16. Bernoulli's Law

#17. Bode's Law

#18. Boyle's Law

LAWS A-B

#19. Charles' Law

#20. Law of Conservation of Matter

#21. Law of Hydrostatics

#22. Lenz's Law

#23. Mendel's Laws

#24. Motion Law: Inertia

LAWS C-M

#25. Motion Law: Action

#26. Motion Law: Reaction

#27. Newton's Law of Gravitation

#28. Ohm's Law

#29. Pascal's Law

LAWS M-P

Use with page 24.

Name

THE SEARCH IS ON

Scientists have inquiring minds. They are always searching for answers. Over time, science has developed a general way of doing investigations and looking for explanations about happenings in the universe. This is called the scientific method or steps to scientific inquiry.

THE DROPPED EGG INVESTIGATION

As Kiko and Thomas were carrying eggs into the house from the grocery store, a huge bolt of thunder struck just outside their door. They were so shocked that they both dropped the eggs. Some eggs stayed in the containers, others dropped out. Some fell on the carpet, others landed on the wooden kitchen floor. They were surprised that all the eggs did not break. Many eggs still in their containers and eggs on the carpet were unbroken. This accident made them curious about what might cause some eggs to break when falling, while others did not break. They guessed that eggs falling on carpet or staying in their containers were less likely to break than eggs flying out of their containers onto a hard floor.

They decided to investigate. They realized that the height from which the eggs dropped and the force of the drop might affect the results. So they chose a precise distance for the drop and decided to let the eggs go gently, with no throwing force. They planned to drop eggs for four different kinds of landings. They thought they should drop enough eggs to avoid chance results. They also planned to do the investigation twice, in two trials, to see if results were similar. They gathered measuring tools, eggs, egg containers, and a sheet to protect the carpet. They planned to drop 12 eggs for each kind of landing. With two trials, there would be a total of 24 eggs dropped in each way. They measured a spot exactly 5 feet off the floor, and marked that spot on the wall. Then they made a table for tallying the results.

Finally they were ready. Kiko stood on a stool and held her arm out level with the mark. She dropped 12 eggs in a carton onto the carpet, and 12 eggs in a carton onto the wooden floor. Next, she dropped 12 eggs, one at a time, onto the carpet. Last, she dropped 12 eggs, one at a time, onto the floor. While she dropped eggs, Thomas kept a tally of the number of eggs broken in each of the four groups. When they finished this trial, they repeated the whole process. They showed their results by creating a summarizing table.

Kiko and Thomas cleaned up their mess and reviewed their results. They came to the conclusion that eggs dropped onto a soft surface in an egg container were the least likely to break. Eggs dropped in the container onto a wooden floor were more likely to break. Just about as likely as this, however, were eggs dropped out of the container onto carpet. The most likely of all to break were eggs dropped outside of a container onto the hard floor. They believed these results showed that the carpet and the containers gave enough protection to the eggs to keep them all from breaking.

After the investigation, they still wondered about breaking eggs. They wanted to know why some eggs didn't break at all, on the carpet, and even on the hard floor. They wondered if eggs in the center of the cartons were more protected than those on the ends. They wondered whether different materials of cartons would make a difference in the number of eggs broken. They got busy planning some more investigations.

Read this report on the *Dropped Egg Investigation.* Then answer the questions about the inquiry process on page 27.

Use with page 27.

Name

Egg-Drop Method	Trial # 1 Number of Eggs Broken	Trial # 2 Number of Eggs Broken	% of Total Eggs Broken in 2 Trials
Eggs in Container, Dropped on Wood Floor	11	9	41.6%
Eggs in Container, Dropped on Carpet	1	2	6.2%
Eggs Dropped on Wood Floor Out of Container	22	24	95.8%
Eggs Dropped on Carpet Out of Container	13	11	50%

Read the investigation described on page 26. Then review the steps in scientific inquiry below. Use the questions to make a record of how these scientists used the process of scientific inquiry.

1. **OBSERVE:** *What observation led to an experiment?*

   _____

2. **ASK QUESTIONS:** *What question(s) did they want to answer?*

   _____

3. **HYPOTHESIZE:** *What was their hypothesis?* _____

4. **PLAN AND CARRY OUT AN INVESTIGATION:** *What plan did they follow?*

   _____

5. **USE TOOLS TO GATHER AND ANALYZE DATA:** *How did they collect the data?*

   What tools and supplies did they use? _____

   _____

6. **ANALYZE AND INTERPRET DATA:** *What were the results?*

   _____

7. **PURPOSE EXPLANATIONS:** *What explanation did they give for the results?*

   _____

8. **COMMUNICATE RESULTS:** *How did they show or share the results?*

   _____

9. **OFFER OTHER QUESTIONS OR IDEAS:** *What other questions or ideas did they offer?*

   _____

10. **MATHEMATICS:** *How did they make use of math in their process?*

   _____

Use with page 26.

Name _____

SORTING OUT BIG IDEAS

Professor Agnes Igneous teaches geology to a group of students. Her students also study many other kinds of science with other scientists. They keep running into some big ideas that stretch into all areas of science. Here are some of the events and facts they have studied. Each of them is related to one or more of the big concepts of science.

Find one or more facts, events, or theories that might be included in each of the 10 books shown. Write the letters on the matching books. *(An item might relate to more than one of the concepts!)*

A. When Agnes jogs on her treadmill, she begins to sweat and the evaporating sweat causes her body to cool so it does not overheat. The body responds to the falling temperature, and blood vessels in her skin contract to reduce the loss of heat.

B. The plants and animals that live in and around Lost Canyon Pond have complex and important relationships with one another. They depend upon each other for survival, and the welfare of each species affects the lives of the others.

C. A shoulder joint is actually a ball and socket. The upper arm bone has a rounded end that fits into a hollow space in the shoulder bone. This allows the shoulder to rotate in a circle.

D. Agnes left her motorcycle outside in the damp San Francisco weather all winter. By spring, the bike was terribly rusty.

E. There are thousands of species of animals—all of different levels of complexity. Fortunately, scientists have developed a classification system that organizes them all, from the simplest to the most complex.

Use with page 29.

F. The sum of total mass (of matter) plus the total energy in the universe always remains the same.

G. When Agnes waters her lawn, the sprinkler does not quite reach to the edge of the lawn. The trees at the outer edge of its lawn get no water soaking into the ground near them. Eventually the trees start to lose their needles and look rather sickly.

H. During six months of research along the ocean, Agnes has watched the rise and fall of the tides. In particular, she has been fascinated by the patterns of the spring tides, neap tides, and tropic tides.

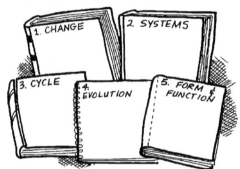

I. When Agnes stepped off the dock into her canoe, the boat took a quick move backward, even though she had stepped forward into the canoe. This quick motion of the boat made her lose her balance and topple into the water.

J. Most scientists believe that interactions among the Earth's land, water, atmosphere, and living organisms have caused a series of changes in the whole Earth system. Some changes, such as those produced by earthquakes, are sudden. But most of the changes, such as mountain-building, take place gradually, over a period of hundreds or thousands of years.

Name

K. The molecules in chocolate milk are not as close together as the molecules in a solid, such as a chocolate bar. With molecules far apart, the substance is more flexible, and so the milk can be poured!

L. As the flame on the burner heats up the teakettle, the water molecules move faster and faster, knocking each other farther apart, until some of them actually change into a gas. These escape the kettle as steam.

M. The fluffy feathers that cover birds have thousands of spaces where air can become trapped and warmed by the bird's body. This ability to trap air in and around the feathers provides a great insulation system for keeping the bird warm as it soars through cold air.

N. A load of passengers climbed into the roller coaster while it was parked at the starting point. Then the coaster began gaining speed, slowly climbing that first big hill.

R. The Periodic Table of Elements arranges all the chemical elements in rows according to their atomic numbers and grouping in columns elements with similar properties.

S. A loaf of bread sat on the counter in its plastic bag. By the end of three weeks, the slices were covered with a lovely blue-green mold.

T. After Agnes takes a nasty crash on her motorbike, her knees and elbows are badly scraped and covered with dirt and germs. Her body responds by sending an army of white blood cells to the areas to destroy the germs.

U. The Big Bang Theory is one explanation of the origin of the universe. According to this theory, the universe began with a major explosion billions of years ago. Since then, the matter from the explosion broke into clumps that became galaxies, which continue to expand and change.

O. Jupiter follows the same path around the sun, over and over. It takes Jupiter 11.86 Earth years to return to the place it started in its orbit.

P. After Agnes eats her favorite chicken taco, it takes many organs working together to digest the food and turn it into the energy she needs to maintain and use her body well.

Q. The charge of any electron in any element or other substance is always a negative charge.

V. Agnes was standing in a pool of water when she turned on her hairdryer. This was not good, because water is a very good conductor or electricity, and the situation was dangerous for her. Fortunately for Agnes, she was wearing shoes with rubber soles because the rubber came between her body and the water—and rubber is a very poor conductor of electricity

W. The thermostat in Agnes's hot tub is set at 100°. When the water temperature falls below 100°, the thermostat sensors trigger the thermostat to turn the heater on until the water again reaches 100°.

Use with page 28.

Name

29

THE WHOLE THING

The natural and designed world is brimming with systems—from minute and simple to monumental and complex. Every system has components (parts), boundaries, and some sort of input and output. Take a close look at a few systems.

A **SYSTEM**
is an organized group
of related parts that form
a whole, working together
to perform one or
more functions.

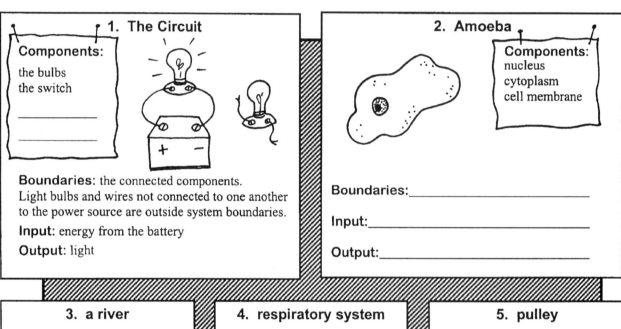

1. The Circuit

Components:
the bulbs
the switch
_____
_____

Boundaries: the connected components.
Light bulbs and wires not connected to one another to the power source are outside system boundaries.

Input: energy from the battery

Output: light

2. Amoeba

Components:
nucleus
cytoplasm
cell membrane

Boundaries:_____

Input:_____

Output:_____

3. a river

Components:

Boundaries:_____

Input:_____

Output:_____

4. respiratory system

Components:

Boundaries:_____

Input:_____

Output:_____

5. pulley

Components:

Boundaries:_____

Input:_____

Output:_____

6. Name 4 other systems:

_____   _____

_____   _____

Name _____

LOOKING FOR ORDER

ORDER
is the predictable behavior of objects, units of matter, events, organisms, or systems. In the natural world, certain events follow others; certain behaviors of organisms and matter can be expected.

ORGANIZATION
is an arrangement of independent items, objects, organisms, units of matter, or systems, joined into a whole system or structure.

1. Lightning strikes a body of water. What will happen to the electric charge?

_____

2. An animal cell is fertilized. What behavior can you expect from the cell?

_____

3. What can you expect from seawater that has become colder and denser due to cold temperatures and evaporation?

_____

4. What behavior can you expect from molten material under high pressure that flows toward a crack in the Earth's crust?

_____

5. As winter comes to the Arctic, the Arctic tern travels 11,000 miles to its breeding ground in Antarctica. What behavior is likely to occur when the Antarctic weather begins to cool and summer comes to the Arctic?

_____

6. One example of organization in nature is the classification of animals. Number these components in order from simplest (1) to the most complex (7).

_____species   _____family

_____phylum   _____order

_____class   _____genus

_____kingdom

7. This is a list of components of living systems. Number them in order of complexity, from the simplest (1) to the most complex (6).

_____tissues   _____cells

_____organs   _____communities

_____populations   _____organisms

8. The Periodic Table arranges elements according to their properties. Which of the following elements would be in a nonmetal group on the Periodic Table? *(Circle them.)*

fluorine	chlorine	iodine
helium	radon	krypton
mercury	titanium	bromine
argon	neon	magnesium

Name _____

WHAT IS IT ABOUT THAT SHAPE?

FORM & FUNCTION
The shape (form) of an organism, object, or system is often related to the operation (function). Frequently the function of an organism, object, or system is very dependent on the shape.

A periscope has a long tube with reflecting mirrors at each end, arranged parallel to each other. The mirrors are at 45° angles to the axis of the tube. The shape and structure of the periscope make it useful to see around corners or to see from distances above or below the object being viewed.

X-rays have very short wave lengths and move very fast. This form gives them great kinetic energy—enough energy to penetrate through soft tissue. These rays can be used to help make pictures of the bones inside bodies.

Starfish have tube-like feet, which are perfect for attaching like suction cups. These structures allow the starfish to grab onto things and move, or to attach to shells while they pull them apart and eat the animals inside.

The form is described. You describe the function made possible by the form.

1. the webbed feet of a duck

     the function ➞ _____

2. the long tubes of kelp, with anchoring ends and gas-filled bladders

     the function ➞ _____

3. the extreme flexibility and stretchable form of copper

     the function ➞ _____

4. the whip-like tail (flagellum) on a bacterium

     the function ➞ _____

5. the layers in a space suit that allow for circulation of liquid

     the function ➞ _____

Use with page 33.

Name

What function or operation is possible because of each form?
Describe the form and the function for each term listed below.

	The Form (or shape)	**The Function** (or operation)
6. planetary orbits		
7. a wedge		
8. any gas		
9. plant roots		
10. a bobsled		
11. cell membrane		
12. convex lens		
13. outer ear		
14. muscle cells		
15. compact disc		
16. plant cell wall		
17. dandelion seeds		
18. hypodermic needle		
19. intestine		
20. microscope		

Hmmm. Very interesting!

Use with page 32.

Name

OPERATION INTERACTION

ENERGY and MATTER
have an extremely close relationship.
They are constantly interacting with one another.
Matter can be changed into energy,
and energy can be transferred to matter.
The total amount of energy plus matter
in the world always stays the same.

The principles of energy and matter are the same in my galaxy, too.

Identify the energy and the matter in each example.
Then describe what will happen when they interact.

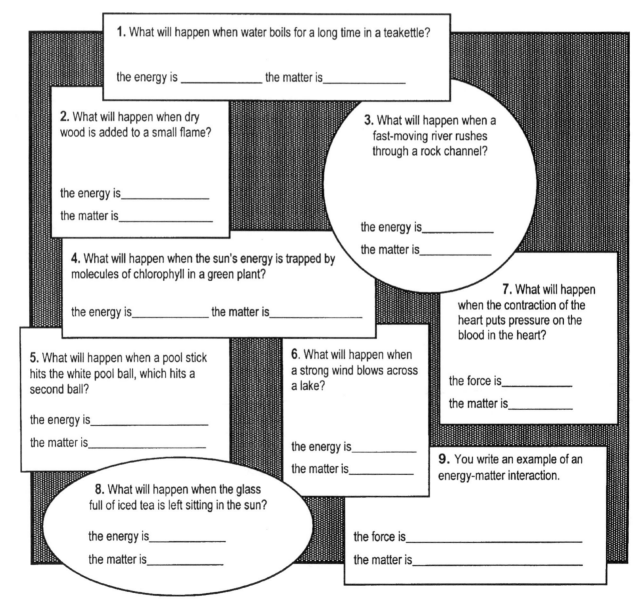

1. What will happen when water boils for a long time in a teakettle?

the energy is _____ the matter is_____

2. What will happen when dry wood is added to a small flame?

the energy is_____
the matter is_____

3. What will happen when a fast-moving river rushes through a rock channel?

the energy is_____
the matter is_____

4. What will happen when the sun's energy is trapped by molecules of chlorophyll in a green plant?

the energy is_____ the matter is_____

5. What will happen when a pool stick hits the white pool ball, which hits a second ball?

the energy is_____
the matter is_____

6. What will happen when a strong wind blows across a lake?

the energy is_____
the matter is_____

7. What will happen when the contraction of the heart puts pressure on the blood in the heart?

the force is_____
the matter is_____

8. What will happen when the glass full of iced tea is left sitting in the sun?

the energy is_____
the matter is_____

9. You write an example of an energy-matter interaction.

the force is_____
the matter is_____

Name _____

CONNECTION INSPECTION

Professor Radon is thinking of cause & effect relationships to use as examples for his students.
Give a close inspection to the connection between the two statements in each pair below.
For each pair of statements, identify the cause with a C. Identify the effect with an E.

CAUSE & EFFECT
A cause is anything that brings about a result.
An effect is the result—the event or situation
that follows from the cause.
Everywhere you look in the physical world,
you can spot cause-effect relationships.

1. _____A. Hot magma which has been trapped beneath Earth's surface begins to cool.
   _____B. The liquid magma solidifies to form intrusive igneous rock.

2. _____A. A drummer strikes a drum; the surface vibrates, producing compressional waves.
   _____B. Compressional waves carry the sound to the drummer's ears.

3. _____A. A highly productive fishing area is created.
   _____B. Upwellings of cold water bring high concentrations of nutrients to the ocean surface.

4. _____A. A mother bird flies around, squawking and madly flapping her wings.
   _____B. A stranger hikes through the territory where a mother bird has a nest of babies.

5. _____A. In its orbit around the Earth, the moon moves into a position that is in a straight
            line with the Earth and sun, on the opposite side of Earth from the sun.
   _____B. A lunar eclipse occurs, meaning that the moon is not visible from Earth.

6. _____A. Guard cells in the epidermis of a leaf swell and open the stoma.
   _____B. Guard cells in the epidermis of a leaf absorb water.

Briefly describe one cause-effect relationship for each area of science:

7. Life Science_____

8. Physical Science _____

9. Earth Science_____

10. Space Science_____

Name _____

TO CHANGE OR NOT TO CHANGE

Search with Dr. Ozzie Moses to find real examples of things that change or stay the same, evolve, or balance. Find examples in the physical world around you.

CONSTANCY
is the opposite of change—a state characterized by lack of variation.

CHANGE
is the process of becoming different.

Describe…

1. a **CHANGE** in physical properties of a material

_____

2. a **CHANGE** in chemical properties of a material

_____

3. a **CHANGE** in state or form of a material

_____

4. a **CHANGE** in position of matter

_____

5. a **CHANGE** in function of an object or organism

_____

6. a **TRANSFER** of energy

_____

Something is about to change....

Identify or describe TWO objects, processes, entities, or characteristics that **remain constant** in the physical world.

7._____

_____

8._____

_____

Use with page 37.

Name _____

EVOLUTION
is a series of changes that cause the
form or function of an object, organism,
or system to be what it currently is.
Some of the changes happen over
a long period of time;
others may happen suddenly.

EQUILIBRIUM
is the state
in which equal forces
occur in opposite directions
and offset (or balance) each other.

9. Describe or identify a system,
object, or organism that has taken the
form it currently has because it has
made a gradual series of changes.

_____

_____

_____

_____

_____

_____

Describe or name 5 examples of
equilibrium in the physical (natural)
world or in the world of human-designed
objects or systems.

10._____

_____

11. _____

_____

12._____

_____

13._____

_____

14._____

_____

Use with page 36.

Name _____

SCIENCE REPEATS ITSELF

A CYCLE
is a series of events or operations that regularly occur and usually lead back to the starting point.

Cycles are everywhere in science. They are so common in the natural world that many of them hardly get noticed. Write a few sentences to explain each of these cycles shown. Then name at least three other cycles in the natural world.

1. MOON PHASES

_____

_____

_____

_____

2. BUTTERFLY LIFE CYCLE

_____

_____

_____

_____

3. THE ROCK CYCLE

_____

_____

_____

_____

_____

_____

4. Name at least 3 other cycles:_____

Name _____

CONCEPTS GET REAL

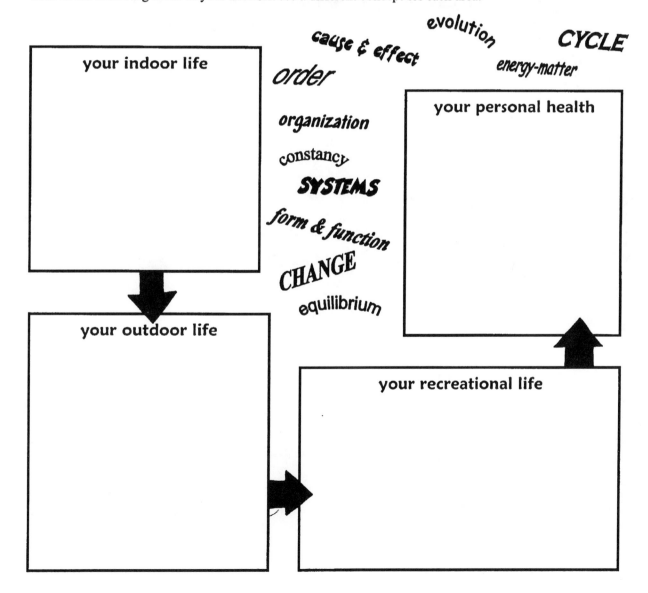

Are there cycles in your health?
Do energy-matter relationships affect any of your hobbies?
Do form and function relationships hang around your classroom?
Are there cause-effect relationships in your backyard?
Can you find any systems in your bathroom?
Is equilibrium at work in your kitchen?

Think about the ways these big ideas of science show up in your life.
Describe one way that ONE of these science concepts shows up in
each of the following areas of your life. Choose a different concept for each area.

your indoor life

cause & effect   evolution   CYCLE

order   energy-matter

organization

constancy

SYSTEMS

form & function

CHANGE

equilibrium

your personal health

your outdoor life

your recreational life

Name

PAY ATTENTION!

Pay close attention to each of these events on this page and page 41.
Use all your senses. Keep a record of your observations.

Watch carefully!

To **OBSERVE**
is to recognize and note facts or occurrences,
or to watch carefully. In scientific inquiry,
observation uses ALL the senses.
Attend to events and facts with your senses
of sight, smell, touch, taste, and hearing.
(But do NOT taste any substances other than foods.)

1. Fill two identical bowls to the top with water, but do not let the water spill over the edge.
   Gently set a ping pong ball into the water of one bowl. Gently set a golf ball into the other bowl.

   What do you observe?_____

2. Spin a hardboiled egg (in the shell) on a hard surface.

   What do you observe?_____

3. Spin an uncooked egg on a hard surface.

   What do you observe?_____

4. Peel a green banana. Slice it into chunks. Eat a chunk.

   What do you observe?_____

5. Hold a fork by its handle, so the fork is hanging down. Bang it with a spoon.

   What do you observe?_____

6. Tie a string around a fork handle. Let the fork hang suspended by the string.
   Bang the fork with a spoon.

   What do you observe?_____

7. Pour some vinegar into a glass cup. Stir in a spoon full of baking soda.

   What do you observe?_____

8. Light a candle. Watch the wick carefully as the candle burns. Watch for 10 minutes.

   What do you observe?_____

Use with page 41.

Name

Pay close attention to each of these events on this page and page 40.
Use all your senses. Keep a record of your observations.

9. Pour very hot water into a metal cup. Place your hands carefully near the cup—but do not touch the cup.

What do you observe?

10. Pour very hot water into a ceramic cup. Place your hands carefully near the cup—but do not touch the cup.

What do you observe?

11. Pour very hot water into a plastic cup. Place your hands carefully near the cup—but do not touch the cup.

What do you observe?

12. Blow up a balloon. Rub it against a wool sweater. Hold it above your hair.

What do you observe?

13. Cook an egg in boiling water for 10 minutes. Drop it into cold water. Peel the egg as soon as you can handle it. Smash the egg and egg white with a fork.

What do you observe?_____

14. Stand in a narrow doorway. Hold your arms out from your sides. Press the backs of your hands hard against the door jam. Keep pressing for 3 full minutes. Step away from the doorway, leaving your arms loosely at your sides.

What do you observe?_____

15. Put some red food coloring in the bottom of a glass jar. Fill the jar two-thirds full of water. Cut two tall stalks of celery. Remove the leaves from the top of one stalk. Leave them on the other. Place the celery stalks in the red water. Check on them in a few hours.

What do you observe?_____

16. Press your first two fingers gently against the right side of your neck just next to your Adam's apple.

What do you observe?_____

17. Cut a large square from a brown paper grocery bag. Rub a piece of cheddar cheese in a streak across the paper. Hold the paper up to the light.

What do you observe?_____

18. Fill 5 glasses of water ½ full with warm water. Mix a teaspoon full of each of these into one of the glasses: salt, pepper, flour, sugar, cinnamon.

What do you observe?_____

Use with page 40.

Name _____

SCIENCE HAS CLASS

To **CLASSIFY**
is to assign objects or processes to a group
or category based on a common characteristic.

Dr. Femur thinks the study of science is a classy profession. She's busy classifying different organisms, events, objects, and processes. Join her in this activity. All the items in each list belong to at least one category. Write a label that could be used to name the classification of those items.

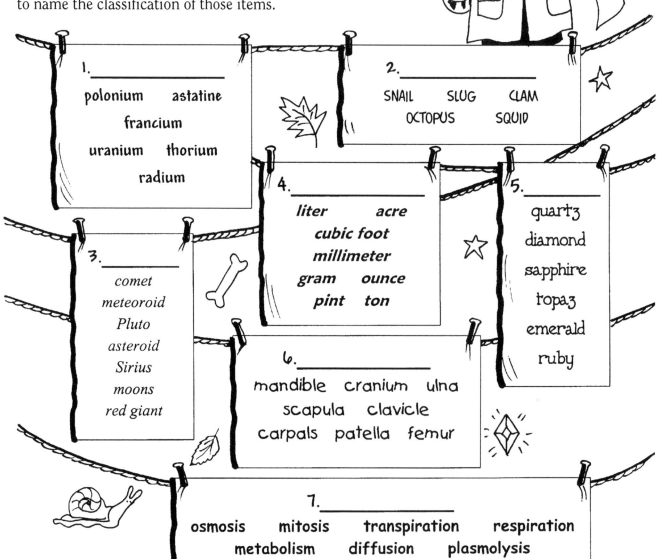

1. _____

polonium   astatine

francium

uranium   thorium

radium

2. _____

SNAIL   SLUG   CLAM

OCTOPUS   SQUID

3. _____

comet
meteoroid
Pluto
asteroid
Sirius
moons
red giant

4. _____

liter   acre
cubic foot
millimeter
gram   ounce
pint   ton

5. _____

quartz
diamond
sapphire
topaz
emerald
ruby

6. _____

mandible   cranium   ulna
scapula   clavicle
carpals   patella   femur

7. _____

osmosis   mitosis   transpiration   respiration
metabolism   diffusion   plasmolysis

Use with page 43.

Name _____

8. Which of these should be in a group labeled
Good Conductors of Electricity?
(Circle them.)

water   wood   glass
rubber   copper   plastic
human body   zinc

9. Which of these should be in a group labeled
Organisms with Bilateral Symmetry?
(Circle them.)

ant   jellyfish   hydra   sponge
lobster   frog   gorilla   octopus
starfish   anemone

abyssal plane
barrier island
ocean ridge
beach
ocean trench
ooze
continental shelf
spit
seamount
tombolo

10. Which of the above would be classified as shore deposits?

_____

_____

_____

mite   scorpion   lobster
beetle   crab   mosquito
centipede
millipede   ladybug

Write three different labels under which these organisms could be classified (with ALL of them belonging to each group).

11. _____

12. _____

13. _____

water   nitrogen   lead   carbon dioxide
wood   iron   sodium chloride   propane

14. Which of the above substances would be classified as compounds? *(Write them.)*

_____

15. Which of the above substances would be classified as organic substances? *(Write them.)*

_____

Use with page 42.

Name _____

MORE THAN JUST A GUESS

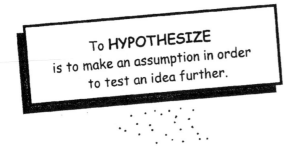

To **HYPOTHESIZE** is to make an assumption in order to test an idea further.

Hypothesizing is more than just a guess. It is a smart guess that you arrive at after making some careful observations of facts or events.

Read each description of an event. Then make a smart guess (a hypothesis) about each one. Make sure the hypothesis is something that could be tested through scientific inquiry.

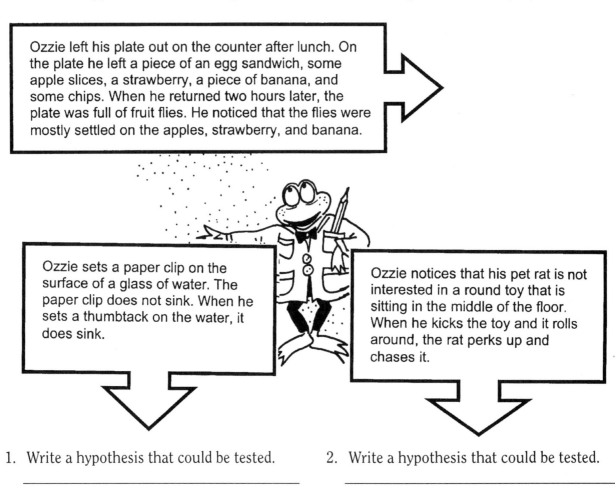

Ozzie left his plate out on the counter after lunch. On the plate he left a piece of an egg sandwich, some apple slices, a strawberry, a piece of banana, and some chips. When he returned two hours later, the plate was full of fruit flies. He noticed that the flies were mostly settled on the apples, strawberry, and banana.

Ozzie sets a paper clip on the surface of a glass of water. The paper clip does not sink. When he sets a thumbtack on the water, it does sink.

Ozzie notices that his pet rat is not interested in a round toy that is sitting in the middle of the floor. When he kicks the toy and it rolls around, the rat perks up and chases it.

1. Write a hypothesis that could be tested.

_____

_____

2. Write a hypothesis that could be tested.

_____

_____

Use with page 45.

Name _____

Read each description of an event. Then make a smart guess (a hypothesis) about each one. Make sure the hypothesis is something that could be tested through scientific inquiry.

Ozzie slices some potatoes, because he intends to make potato chips. He lets them soak in very salty water. (He thinks this will make them into nice, salty chips when he fries them.) When he comes back several hours later to fry the chips, the slices are very limp.

When Ozzie is getting ready to wash dishes, he mistakenly bangs two pot lids together. He notices the sound. Then, while washing the lids, he bangs them together under water. He is surprised that the sound is louder and clearer than before.

4. Write a hypothesis that could be tested.

_____

_____

5. Write a hypothesis that could be tested.

_____

_____

Ozzie watched a friend do a magic trick. The friend filled a cup of water almost to the top with cold water. Then she floated a big ice cube on the top. The friend laid a piece of wet string across the ice cube. Then she sprinkled salt over the string and waited three minutes. When she picked up the ends of the string, she also picked up the ice cube because it stuck to the string.

Ozzie had a liter bottle full of water. He wanted to empty the water. He turned the bottle upside down. It took a very long time to empty. The water just did not seem to want to come out, even though he was holding the bottle directly upside down.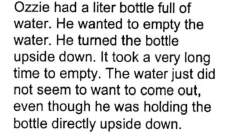

6. Write a hypothesis that could be tested.

_____

_____

7. Write a hypothesis that could be tested.

_____

_____

Use with page 44.

Name _____

YOU DO THE MATH

To MEASURE
is to compare an object to some standard quantity in order to find out an amount or an extent.

USE NUMBERS
Numbers are used constantly in science. Numbers allow for measurements and they describe amounts.

What unit would you choose to measure . . .

1. the distance from your home to Paris, France?

_____

2. the fuel in your gas tank?_____

3. the length of a fruit fly?_____

4. the water in a swimming pool?_____

5. the temperature of a milkshake?_____

6. the capacity of your school locker?_____

7. the length of the school day?_____

8. the length of a shoelace?_____

9. the length of your friend's tongue_____

10. the weight of an elephant?_____

Find each of these measurements:

11. the distance from your nose to your knee_____

12. the capacity of your backpack

_____

13. the weight of all your school books

_____

14. the circumference of your head

_____

15. the temperature inside your refrigerator

_____

Professor Radon did a tug-of-war experiment. He wanted to find out if the number of people pulling on one side was more a factor in winning than the weight of the people. He marked the center of the rope. Then he put six people on one side, and ten people on the other side. The total weight of the six was greater than the total weight of the ten.

16. Describe the ways that the professor used math in his experiment.

_____

_____

Name _____

SO WHAT?

So, Professor Igneous has finished some investigations. She has some results. What will she do with those results? What do they mean? What has she learned? Two processes that follow the collection of data in an inquiry are inferring and predicting. Dr. Igneous can use the information she gathered to draw some conclusions and make some judgments about what else might happen.

Read her results.
Then make your own inferences and predictions.

> **To INFER**
> is to draw a conclusion based on facts or information gained from an inquiry.

> **To predict**
> is to foretell what is likely to happen based on an observation or experiment.

THE SINGING GLASSES

The Experiment: Testing sounds produced by banging a metal spoon against glasses filled with different amounts of water. The experiment used 5 glasses, each the same size and shape—8 inches tall. They were filled to the heights of 1, 2, 3, 4, and 5 inches.

Results: The glass filled to 1 inch produced the highest sound. Next highest was the 2-inch full glass; third highest was the 3-inch full glass. Next highest was the 4-inch full glass. The 5-inch full glass had the lowest sound.

1. What can you infer about the relationship of sounds to the amounts of water in the glasses?

_____

_____

2. What kind of a sound will probably result from a glass that is full to the brim?

_____

A MAP OF THE TONGUE

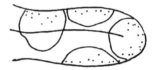

The Experiment: Tasting several food items by touching them (with cotton swabs) on each of four areas of the tongue: front, back, and sides.

Results: She tasted the honey, molasses, and sugar on the tip of her tongue. On the sides, she tasted the lemon juice and vinegar. On the back of her tongue, she tasted the bitter black tea.

3. What can you infer about the tongue from these results?

_____

_____

4. On which part of her tongue is Dr. Igneous likely to get the full taste of pickle juice?

_____

Name _____

NOT THE REAL THING

To USE MODELS
is to use some sort of a structure
or scheme that visually represents
real objects or events.

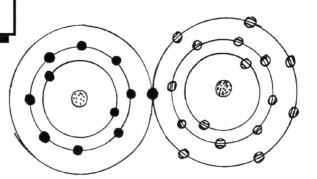

Many models are three-dimensional.
Imagine that Professor Aster Oid's
representation of two atoms is
three-dimensional. Use information
from the model to fill in the blanks
in his explanation.

1. This model shows a chemical reaction between the elements _____ and _____.

2. _____ has only 1 electron in its outer ring, making it _____(stable, unstable).

3. _____ has only 7 electrons in its outer ring, making it _____(stable, unstable).

4. When the two chemicals combine, the element _____ takes the extra electron from

   _____. This way, its last ring is filled. The other element, _____, has

   lost one electron, but now its outer orbit (second ring) is full. Both elements are happy with the

   combination!

5. Which formula is a model (representation)
   of a chemical reaction between
   magnesium and chlorine
   to produce magnesium chloride?

A. $Mn + 2\,C + 2\,O = MnC_2O_2$

B. $Mn + 2O = MnO_2$

C. $Mg + 2\,Cl = MgCl_2$

D. $3\,Md + Cl = Md_3\,Cl$

E. $Mg + Cl = MgCl$

Name _____

SO, WHY DOES THE EGG FLOAT?

Professor Radon has been trying to get an egg to float. He has succeeded, but no one can learn anything from his experiment if he does not share it and try to explain its meaning. Scientific discoveries, answers to questions, and results of inquiries do not do much good if they are kept secret.

> **To INTERPRET**
> is to explain or tell the meaning of the results in an experiment.
> **To COMMUNICATE**
> is to tell or show others the process and results of the experiment.

Read about Professor Radon's inquiry and the results. Then help with the explanation.

Observation: A friend showed him an egg floating in water, but Reginald could not get an egg to float. Then, he remembered how easily he could float in the ocean.

Hypothesis: Objects will float more easily in salt water than in fresh water.

Experimental Process: He filled a glass two-thirds full with fresh water. He set an egg in the glass. Then he stirred in some salt. He kept adding salt and stirring.

Results: At first, the egg sank. As he added more salt, the egg floated higher and higher.

1. **INTERPRETATION:** Explain the meaning of Professor Radon's results.

   _____

   _____

2. **EVIDENCE:** An explanation or interpretation should be based on evidence. What evidence led you to the explanation you gave?

   _____

3. **FURTHER QUESTIONS:** A good inquiry usually raises new questions, even while it provides some answers. Write at least one question you have after reading Dr. Radon's results.

   _____

Name

49

IN PURSUIT OF ANSWERS

> ## To DESIGN AN EXPERIMENT
> is to make a plan to find an answer for a question or to test a hypothesis.
> The plan includes all the steps to take and equipment to be used in the process.

Dr. Igneous wants to make frozen juice pops for her picnic. She is curious about how long it will take for the pops to freeze. She knows that juice is a solution—not a pure substance. So, she wonders how the freezing time will compare to the freezing time of water. She assumes that the juice (a solution) will take longer to freeze than water.

Agnes makes a plan to answer her question about the freezing time of juice pops. She gets five small paper cups and five wooden sticks for "handles" for her frozen pops. She finds a measuring cup and measuring spoons, and a bigger spoon for stirring. Then, she opens a bottle of grape juice. She also has a pitcher of water handy, and a pen for writing on the cups.

On one cup, she writes *water*, and fills the cup with water. On the next cup, she writes *pure juice*. She fills this with juice. On the third cup, she writes *one-half juice*. She fills the measuring cup to the ½ cup mark with juice, and adds water to the 1-cup mark. After mixing this, she pours some into the third cup to fill it. On the fourth cup, she writes *one-fourth juice*. After emptying the measuring cup, she fills it to the ¼ cup mark with juice, then to the 1-cup mark with water. She stirs this and pours some in to fill the cup. She writes *one-eighth juice* on the last cup. In the empty measuring cup, she measures two tablespoons of juice. She fills the cup to the 1-cup mark and stirs. Then, she pours this mixture into the last cup.

All the cups are placed in the freezer. Every 10 minutes, she will check the pops to see how the freezing is coming along. She will keep a record of what happens for each of the five cups.

1. What is her hypothesis?_____

2. What are the variables in the experiment? _____

3. What variable is controlled? _____

4. What measurement tools does she use? _____

5. How does her plan include the use of numbers? _____

Use with page 51.

Name _____

Professor Igneous hates ants-especially on her food! She remembers a picnic once where the ants attacked her sticky sugar-apple cake. She hopes ants do not come to tomorrow's picnic at all. But, just in case they are around, she wishes she could choose food that would NOT attract ants.

What foods do ants like best? What foods might they avoid?

Design an experiment that would help Professor Igneous answer this question.

Hmmm, kibble-burger!

QUESTION: _____

HYPOTHESIS: _____

TOOLS & SUPPLIES: _____

_____

STEPS FOR THE INVESTIGATION:

_____

_____

_____

_____

_____

_____

_____

_____

_____

HOW RESULTS WILL BE SHOWN:

_____

_____

Use with page 50.

Name _____

PROCEED WITH CARE

Professor Moses is constantly reminding his students about proper lab procedures. He has asked some of them to make a poster about safe behaviors in the lab. This is the poster his students prepared. It has some flaws.

Circle the number of any rules that are correct. Fix the rules that are not correct by crossing out wrong information and writing it correctly.

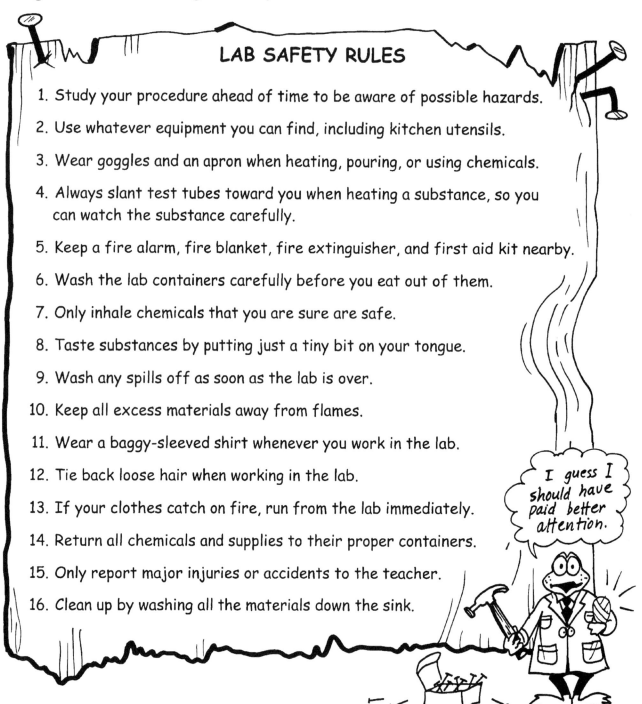

LAB SAFETY RULES

1. Study your procedure ahead of time to be aware of possible hazards.

2. Use whatever equipment you can find, including kitchen utensils.

3. Wear goggles and an apron when heating, pouring, or using chemicals.

4. Always slant test tubes toward you when heating a substance, so you can watch the substance carefully.

5. Keep a fire alarm, fire blanket, fire extinguisher, and first aid kit nearby.

6. Wash the lab containers carefully before you eat out of them.

7. Only inhale chemicals that you are sure are safe.

8. Taste substances by putting just a tiny bit on your tongue.

9. Wash any spills off as soon as the lab is over.

10. Keep all excess materials away from flames.

11. Wear a baggy-sleeved shirt whenever you work in the lab.

12. Tie back loose hair when working in the lab.

13. If your clothes catch on fire, run from the lab immediately.

14. Return all chemicals and supplies to their proper containers.

15. Only report major injuries or accidents to the teacher.

16. Clean up by washing all the materials down the sink.

Name _____

APPENDIX

CONTENTS

TERMS FOR SCIENCE CONCEPTS & PROCESSES

cause — anything that brings about a result

change — the process of becoming different

classify — assign objects of processes to a group or category based on a common characteristic or group of characteristics

communicate — tell or show others the process and results of an experiment

constancy — a state characterized by a lack of variation

cycle — a series of events or operations that regularly occur and usually lead back to the starting point

effect — a result; an event or situation that follows from a cause

form — the shape of an organism, object, or system

form & function — the relationship between the shape (form) of an organism, object, or system, and the operation (function) of the organism, object, or system

function — the operation of an organism, object, or system

energy-matter — the close relationships and interactions between matter and energy

equilibrium — the state in which equal forces occur in opposite directions and offset each other

evolution — a series of changes that cause the form or function of an object, organism, or system to be what it currently is

hypothesize — to make an assumption in order to test it further

infer — to draw a conclusion based on facts or information gained from an inquiry

interpret — to explain or tell the meaning of the results in an experiment

law — a rule that describes the behavior of something in nature

measure — to compare an object, amount, or change to some standard quantity in order to find out an amount or an extent

model — a structure or scheme that visually represents real objects or events

observe — recognize and note facts or occurrences; to watch carefully

order — the predictable behavior of objects, units of matter, events, organisms, or systems

organization — the arrangement of independent items, objects, organisms, units of matter, or systems, joined into a whole system or structure

predict — foretell what is likely to happen based on an observation or experiment

scientific inquiry — a way of doing investigations and looking for explanations about happenings in the physical world; a series of steps generally followed in looking for answers to questions in science

system — an organized group of related parts that form a whole, working together to perform one or more functions

theory — an explanation based on many observations during repeated experiments

FIELDS OF SCIENCE

A Brief Summary of the Areas Studied by Some Branches of Science

aeronautics — the operation of aircraft

agronomy — soils and crop production

anatomy — the structure of organisms

anthropology — human culture

archaeology — past human cultures

astronomy — celestial bodies and their motions

bacteriology — bacteria and their relation to medicine, health, and agriculture

biology — living organisms and life processes

botany — plants

chemistry — properties, structure, and composition of substances, and the changes they undergo

climatology — climate

cryogenics — behavior of substances at very low temperatures

cytology — life history, structure, function, pathology, and reproduction of cells

ecology — the interrelationship of organisms and their environment

economics — production, distribution, and consumption of goods and services

embryology — embryos and their development

entomology — insects

genetics — heredity and variations in organisms

geography — earth features and their relationship to the living things on earth

geology — history of the earth; rocks

geometry — properties, measurements, and relationships of points, lines, angles, surface shapes, and solids

hematology — blood and blood-forming organs

histology — living tissues

hydrology — water in the atmosphere and on the land surface, in soil, and rocks

ichthyology — fish

immunology — causes and responses of immunity

linguistics — human speech

marine biology — ocean life

meteorology — weather

microbiology — living organisms too small to be seen with the naked eye

mineralogy — properties and classification of minerals

morphology — structure and form of plants and animals

neurology — nervous system

oceanography — ocean characteristics, processes, behaviors, and life

oncology — tumors

ophthalmology — structure, functions, and diseases of the eye

ornithology — birds

paleontology — fossils and the life from past geological periods

petrology — origin, structure, properties, classification, and history of rocks

physics — matter and energy and their interactions

physiology — matter and energy and their interactions

political science — government

psychiatry — medicine of behavioral, emotional, and mental disorders

psychology — the mind and behavior

radiology — use of radiant energy to diagnose and treat diseases

rheumatology — diseases characterized by inflammation and pain in joints or muscles

seismology — earthquakes

sociology — behavior of human groups and of humans in groups

taxonomy — scientific classification of plants and animals

zoology — animals

Basic Skills/Science Concepts & Processes 6-8+   Copyright ©2002 by Incentive Publications, Inc., Nashville, TN.

SCIENCE CONCEPTS & PROCESSES SKILLS TEST

Each correct answer is worth 1 point. Total possible points = 66

1–16: Which field of science is related to each of the topics below? Write a letter from the list.

_____ 1. insects
_____ 2. blood
_____ 3. rocks
_____ 4. fish
_____ 5. heredity
_____ 6. diseases
_____ 7. plants
_____ 8. cells
_____ 9. soils and crops
_____ 10. the human mind
_____ 11. organisms and their environment
_____ 12. substances at very low temperatures
_____ 13. the structure of matter
_____ 14. the structure of organisms
_____ 15. prehistoric life
_____ 16. functions of living matter

A. paleontology
B. ornithology
C. histology
D. entomology
E. physiology
F. hematology
G. chemistry
H. anatomy
I. psychology
J. agronomy
K. cytology
L. physics
M. botany
N. petrology
O. geology
P. genetics
Q. pathology
R. ecology
S. cryogenics
T. ichthyology

17–26: Decide which statements below are true. Circle their numbers.

17. Technology is the use of scientific discoveries.
18. Math is rarely a part of scientific investigations.
19. Most scientific ideas are absolute, and not subject to change.
20. Fields of scientific study rarely overlap with one another.
21. Scientists researching the same problem often find and publish different results.
22. A scientific law is an explanation based on many observations during repeated experiments.
23. Scientists disregard personal beliefs and ethics when they carry out scientific inquiry.
24. There is no right or wrong way to solve a scientific problem.
25. Scientists use models to represent actual objects, systems, or ideas.
26. A scientific theory becomes a law when it has been sufficiently tested and validated.

27. Which of the following is theory and not a law? *(Choose one answer.)*

A. A warm object placed in a cold place will cool, and objects around it will become warmer.

B. Earth has an outer shell of rigid plates that move about on a layer of hot, flowing rock.

C. An object at rest will remain at rest unless acted on by an outside force.

D. Pressure applied to a fluid in a closed container exerts equal force throughout the container.

28–30: Write a rule for science lab safety related to each of the following behaviors or lab situations.

28. holding a test tube while heating _____

29. what to do if your clothing catches fire _____

30. tasting substances used in experiments _____

31. Write a benefit and a consequence for the development of the jet engine.

Benefit: _____

_____

Consequence: _____

_____

helium   nitrogen

neon   krypton

radon   argon

oxygen

32. Write a title to show one group in which all the above substances could be classified.

33–35: Circle one correct answer.

33. Dr. Fleming's 1920 discovery that enabled the cure of many diseases was the discovery of
    a. antiseptics.   b. antibiotics.   c. anesthetics.   d. DNA.

34. Which was invented most recently?
    a. telescopes   b. the fax machine   c. the microchip   d. the electric light bulb

35. Which was discovered first?
    a. gravity   b. electromagnetic waves   c. quarks   d. penicillin

36–44: Which page (below) describes each of these theories or laws? Write A, B, C, D, E, or N (for none).

_____ 36. Law of Motion (Inertia)
_____ 37. Law of Conservation of Matter
_____ 38. Law of Motion (Reaction)
_____ 39. Archimedes' Principle
_____ 40. Continental Drift Theory
_____ 41. Plate Tectonics Theory
_____ 42. Boyle's Law
_____ 43. Theory of Relativity
_____ 44. Heliocentric Theory

A. Earth's continents have been in different positions through geologic time.

B. A moving object or an object at rest resists change in velocity.

C. Mass is neither gained nor lost in a chemical reaction.

D. The sun is the center of the solar system, with planets revolving around it.

E. Decreasing the volume of a gas will increase the pressure it exerts.

45–52. Which concept (from the chart) is shown by each of the examples below? Write the code letter or letters of one concept to match each example. (There may be more than one right answer for each.)

BIG IDEAS

systems (SYS)
order (ORD)
organization (ORG)
form & function (F&F)
energy-matter (E-M)
change (CH)
constancy (CON)
cycle (CY)
equilibrium (EQ)
evolution (EV)
cause & effect (C&E)

_____ 45. Summer follows spring.

_____ 46. A tidal wave results from an earthquake.

_____ 47. The heart, blood vessels, and blood work together to circulate nutrients around the body.

_____ 48. The charge of an electron is always negative.

_____ 49. When a candle is lit, the wick ignites and wax begins to melt and vaporize.

_____ 50. A beaver's large, sharp teeth are good for cutting tree branches.

_____ 51. A skater's foot pushes the skate blade backward, and the skater glides forward.

_____ 52. Rain and snow fall to the earth. The run-off collects in rivers, lakes, and oceans. Water evaporates from these bodies of water and returns to the atmosphere as water vapor.

53–58: Give an example for each of the following:

53. a cycle in life science _____

54. the function of an object is made possible by its form _____

_____

55. a cause-effect relationship in earth or space science _____

_____

56. a technological advance that led to a scientific discovery _____

_____

57. a technological invention that led to a problem for individuals or society _____

_____

58. a societal need that led to the development of a new technology _____

_____

Agnes left her bike, scooter, and skates outdoors for months during the damp winter. In the spring, the scooter was very rusty. The bike had some rust, but not as much as the scooter. The skates had no rust at all.

59. Read the observation. Write a hypothesis that could be tested through scientific inquiry.

_____

_____

_____

_____

60–65: Read the experiment. Write your answer to each question.

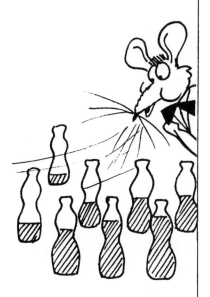

Reginald has just finished an experiment with sound. When he tapped a metal spoon against glasses of water, he discovered that the tapping produced a higher sound as the water got lower in the glasses. So he assumed that the same thing would be true if he blew across the tops of bottles filled to different levels.

He found 8 glass bottles of the exact same size, shape, and material. He filled them to varying levels with water. He labeled the bottles #1 - #8. *(The bottle with the least amount of water was #1.)* He measured the different heights of the water and kept a record of the measurements.

Then, he began blowing. He kept a record of the pitches of sound produced *(according to how they related to the other sounds).* He found that the sounds got higher and higher as the bottles got more full. The bottle with the least amount of water produced the lowest sound. The bottle with the highest level of water produced the highest sound.

60. What observation led to the investigation?_____

61. What was his hypothesis? _____

62. How did he use math in his experiment? _____

63. What results did Reginald get from his experiment? _____

_____

64. What variables were controlled in the experiment? _____

_____

65. What sound would result if one of the bottles was empty? _____

66. What explanation would you suggest for Reginald's results?_____

SKILLS TEST ANSWER KEY

1. D
2. F
3. O
4. T
5. P
6. Q
7. M
8. K
9. J
10. I
11. R
12. S
13. L
14. H
15. A
16. E
17–26: Circle the following numbers to indicate the true statements: 17, 21, 24, 25, 26
27. B
28–30: Answers may vary somewhat. The general idea of each answer is given here:
28. Hold the test tube pointing away from yourself or anyone else.
29. Do not run. Roll up in a safety blanket or heavy coat.
30. Never taste substances in the laboratory, except for food substances.
31. Answers will vary. Possibilities: Benefit: fast travel; Consequences: pollution, noise, safety problems with jet airplanes
32. elements or gases
33. b
34. c
35. a
36. B
37. C
38. N
39. N
40. A

41. N
42. E
43. N
44. D
45. ORD
46. C&E or E-M
47. SYS
48. CON
49. CH or E-M or C&E
50. F&F
51. EQ or C&E
52. CY or CH

53–58: Answers will vary. Check to see that student has given a reasonable and accurate example for each.

59–66: Answers will vary. Answers given here are possibilities.
59. Different substances rust at different rates. Or, different substances are more or less susceptible to rusting.
60. The previous experiment showed that higher sounds came from less water in the glasses.
61. A higher sound would result as water levels decreased.
62. He measured heights of water and counted bottles.
63. The pitch was higher as the water levels increased.
64. The size, material, shape of the bottles; the person doing the blowing
65. The sound would be lower than any of the others.
66. Answers will vary—accept any thoughtful explanation, whether or not it is accurate scientifically.

ANSWERS

pages 10–11

1. b
2. a
3. b
4. c
5. a
6. b
7. a
8. c
9. a, b, c
10. b
11. E & S
12. L
13. Soc
14. P
15. P or E & S
16. L
17. M
18. P or E & S
19. L
20. Soc
21. M
22. M or Soc
23. E & S
24. L

pages 12–13

1. c
2. a
3. d
4. d
5. b
6. b
7. c
8. c
9. a
10. c
11. a
12. a
13. a
14. c
15. b
16. d
17. d
18. a
19. c
20. b
21. c
22. a
23. d
24. a
25. b
26. d

27. Answers will vary. Some possibilities are:
   a. chemist or physicist
   b. anatomist or biologist or archaeologist
   c. geologist or archaeologist
   d. botanist
   e. astronomer, rocket scientist

pages 14–15

1. B
2. Y
3. F
4. D
5. G
6. Z
7. BB
8. AA
9. K
10. W
11. T
12. P
13. M
14. E
15. L
16. H
17. C
18. V
19. DD
20. CC
21. Q
22. J
23. X
24. R
25. I
26. S
27. U
28. O
29. N
30. A

pages 16–17

Answers on these two pages will vary. Check to see that student has responded to at least 15 of the discoveries and/or inventions by describing a reasonable change that has resulted.

pages 18–19

1. b
2. b
3. a
4. a, b, d
5. b
6. d
7. c
8. d
9. c
10. a
11. b, c
12. d
13. d
14. a, b, c
15. b
16. a

page 20

Answers will vary. Check to see that student has changed or corrected the statements with reasonable changes. The answers provided here are possible changes:
1. Individuals CAN have an effect.
2. The effects of natural hazards cannot be eliminated, but can be alleviated by science.
3. Technology has some risks and negative consequences.
4. There are many ways to reduce risks.
5. Science still cannot meet all human needs.
6. Research IS affected by politics.
7. There ARE ways to reduce the risks.
8. Hazards CAN be caused by human activities.
9. Prescription drugs have healing effects, but some can have harmful effects too.
10. Some inventions bring more benefits that hazards.
11. Science and technology will never solve all human problems
12. Some natural substances are safe and healthy; some are not.
13. Regular exercise is ONE IMPORTANT thing needed.
14. Science can protect people from SOME natural disasters.
15. Scientists CANNOT freely do research on humans.
16. Use of tobacco products DOES have a connection to illness.

page 21

Student answers will vary. Examine the answers to see that each describes accurately one way science is present in each place.

page 22

1. A, B, D, E, F
2–5. Answers will vary. Check to see that each answer gives a clear and accurate example of the statement.

page 23

Student answers will vary. Check to see that student has given a thoughtful and reasonable benefit and consequence for each invention.

pages 24–25

Student answers will vary. Make sure student has the general idea of the theory or law. It is acceptable if the theories and laws are stated in their simplist forms.

1. Big Bang Theory-the universe formed as the result of a giant, violent explosion
2. Cell Theory- the cell is the basic structural and functional unit of all animals and plants
3. Chaos Theory-systems behave unpredictably and randomly even though they clearly appear to be governed by well-understood laws of physics
4. Continental Drift Theory-continents were once all one land mass, but have moved from their original locations
5. Electromagnetic Theory-electric and magnetic fields act together to produce electromagnetic waves of radiant energy
6. Theory of Evolution-all species of plant and animal life developed gradually from a small number of common ancestors
7. Germ Theory-infectious diseases are caused by microorganisms
8. Heliocentric Theory-the earth and other planets revolve around the sun
9. Plate Tectonics Theory-the earth has an outer shell of rigid plates that move about on a layer of hot, flowing rock
10. Theory of Relativity-observations of time and space are not absolute, they are relative to the observer
11. Quark Theory-the nucleus of atoms (the protons and neutrons) are made up of subatomic particles
12. String Theory-the fundamental particles that make up objects (electrons and quarks) are tiny strings that vibrate in different patterns
13. Theory of Superconductivity-the electrical resistance of a substance disappears at very low temperatures
14. Archimedes' Principle-an object that is partly or fully immersed in a liquid is pushed upward by a force equal to the weight of the liquid that the object displaces
15. Beer's Law-no substance is perfectly transparent; some of the light passing through any substance is always absorbed
16. Bernoulli's Law-the pressure of a fluid increases as its velocity decreases, and decreases as its velocity increases
17. Bodes' Law-a way to calculate approximate distances of the planets from the sun

18. Boyle's Law-the pressure of a gas increases as the volume of gas decreases if there is no temperature change
19. Charles' Law-the ratio between the volume of a gas and its temperature remains constant if the pressure does not change OR a gas's volume expands by the same ratio of its original volume with each degree of rise in temperature
20. Law of Conservation of Matter-The mass of all substances in a chemical reaction is the same after the reaction as before the reaction. In a chemical reaction, matter is not gained or lost.
21. Law of Hydrostatics-the pressure caused by the weight of a column of fluid is determined by the height of the column
22. Lenz's Law-when electric current is created by a changing magnetic field, the current creates its own magnetic field in a direction that opposes the change in the original magnetic field.
23. Mendel's Laws- heredity characteristics are determined by units called genes which occur in pairs
24. Law of Motion: Inertia-an object at rest stays unless a force acts on it to move it; a moving object will continue moving at the same velocity and in the same direction unless a force acts to change it
25. Law of Motion: Action-the amount of force needed to change the speed of an object depends on the mass of the object and the acceleration required
26. Law of Motion: Reaction-for every action (or force) there is an equal and opposite action (or force)
27. Newton's Law of Gravitation-the gravitational force between two objects is proportional to the size of their masses
28. Ohm's Law-electromotive force equals the electric current multiplied by the resistance in a circuit
29. Pascal's Law-pressure that is applied to a fluid enclosed in a container is transmitted with equal force throughout the container

pages 26–27

Answers will vary.
1. Eggs dropped by accident did not all break.
2. Why did some eggs break and others did not?
3. Eggs dropped in a container or on a carpet will be less likely to break than eggs dropped on a hard floor.
4. They dropped 24 eggs in each of 4 different ways-all from the same height and with the same force.

5. They used eggs, egg containers, measuring tape. They collected data by counting and tallying broken eggs.
6. The eggs in containers and eggs dropped on the carpet broke in smaller numbers than eggs dropped on the hard floor.
7. The eggs were protected by the containers and the soft carpet.
8. a table
9. Why didn't all the eggs break? Did the position of the egg in the container make a difference? Would the material of the egg container make a difference?
10. Math was used to count eggs to be used, count eggs broken, and to measure the height of the drop. Math was used to calculate percentages of eggs broken.

pages 28–29

Answers may vary. Make sure each letter A–W is assigned to one of these books, and that the choice of the placement makes sense or can be explained by the student.
1. D, L, N, S, A, G, J
2. B, P, E, T, C, H
3. H, O
4. J, U
5. C, K, M
6. F, Q
7. G, V, T, D
8. A, I, W
9. E, R
10. N, V, I, Q, L, P

page 30

Answers may vary.
1. Other components: battery, wires
2. Boundaries: the cell membrane forms the boundary
   Input: food, water
   Output: energy, wastes
3. Components: any streams that flow into the river
   Boundaries: determined by water that flows into the river; other flowing water is out of boundary
   Input: water flowing from melting snow, streams, tributaries; silt and debris carried by river
   Output: energy created by flowing water, water vapor evaporating
4. Components: lungs, diaphragm, bronchial tubes, trachea, mouth, bronchioles, alveoli
   Boundaries: limited to these organs
   Input: air containing oxygen for cells
   Output: air containing wastes (carbon dioxide)

5. Components: wheels and rope or chain
Boundaries: limited to the wheels and rope or chain
Input: pulling energy exerted by an outside force
Output: increased work or energy made possible by design of pulley
6. Answers will vary.

page 31

Answers may vary somewhat on 1–5.
1. It will travel through water.
2. It will begin to divide.
3. It will sink.
4. It will erupt through the crack.
5. They will fly back to the Arctic.
6. 1–6–5–7–3–4–2
7. 2–3–5–1–6–4
8. fluorine, chlorine, iodine, helium, radon, krypton, bromine, argon, neon

pages 32–33

Answers will vary. Allow any answers that give reasonable and accurate descriptions of form and function.
1. act as paddles to help duck swim and dive
2. anchors plant to bottom to keep it from washing away; floats near surface to get light
3. can be made into wires or shaped into objects
4. helps the organism move
5. keeps body temperatures normal
6. Form: elliptical; Function: changes in seasons and positions of planets
7. Form: narrow at one end, widening toward other end; Function: fits into small spaces and spreads something open
8. Form: molecules are far apart; Function: allows substance to spread to fit a container
9. Form: long, skinny, flexible: Function: reach into cracks and around obstacles to get water and food
10. Form: sleek, smooth, bullet-shaped; Function: shape with little wind resistance enhances its speed

11. Form: solid; Function: holds in cell material OR Form: very thin, permeable; Function: allows substances to pass through it
12. Form: thick in the middle; Function: refracts light rays toward each other and thus magnifies objects
13. Form: cup-shaped; Function: directs sound into inner ear
14. Form: long and skinny; Function: allows for stretching and movement
15. Form: flat, hard plastic; Function: laser can "write" on it, durable, long-lasting
16. Form: rigid, hard; Function: supports plant stem
17. Form: fluffy top; Function: floats through air to carry seeds where they can germinate
18. Form: long, skinny, hollow; Function: holds liquid, punctures skin and tissue
19. Form: long, skinny, flexible, muscular; Function: wraps around other organs, squeezes substances along
20. Form: constructed with magnifying lenses and lights; Function: allows tiny things to be seen

page 34

1. Water turns to water vapor (evaporates). energy-heat; matter-water
2. Fire will grow bigger. energy-heat; matter-wood
3. Rock will wear away. energy-power of moving water; matter-rock
4. The plant will make food (photosynthesis). energy-sun; matter-plant cells or chlorophyll
5. The second ball will move and the white ball may stop or change direction. energy-human muscle power, transferred to stick, transferred to white ball; matter-pool balls and stick
6. Waves are created on the surface. energy-wind power; matter-water
7. Blood will flow out of the heart to the body. energy-heart pumping; matter-blood
8. The ice will melt and the tea will warm. energy-sun; matter-ice and tea
9. Answers will vary.

page 35

1. A. C B. E
2. A. C B. E
3. A. E B. C
4. A. E B. C
5. A. C B. E
6. A. E B. C
7–10. Answers will vary. Check to see that student has adequately described four cause-effect relationships, one pertinent to each area listed.

pages 36–37

Answers will vary. Check to see that student has described examples that accurately demonstrate the four concepts listed.

page 38

1–3. Answers will vary. Answers should each give an accurate summary of the cycle shown.
1. Moon Phases: As the moon revolves around the earth, it changes position in relation to the earth and so looks different in different places. It moves from a full moon toward 3/4 visible, then 1/2 visible, then 1/4 visible, then to a new moon (none visible), then 1/4 visible, 1/2 visible, 3/4 visible, back to a full moon.
2. Butterfly Life Cycle: Adult butterfly lays eggs; eggs hatch into a worm-like caterpillar; caterpillar spins a cocoon; butterfly emerges from the cocoon.
3. Rock Cycle: Through cooling, compacting under pressure, weathering, and erosion, the three different rock forms can change to other forms of rock.
4. See that student has named three other cycles.

page 39

All answers will vary.
Check to see that student has addressed 4 different concepts and given a clear example related to each life area.

pages 40–41

Answers will vary somewhat. These are general ideas about what will probably be observed.

1. Ping pong ball will float; golf ball will sink.
2. Spins smoothly and evenly.
3. Spins less smoothly-is wobbly.
4. Feels dry in mouth; "pinches" mouth.
5. Fork makes a dull sound.
6. Fork makes a ringing sound; fork swings.
7. Mixture bubbles and fizzes.
8. The wick curls; wax vaporizes; smoke rises; heat travels out from candle; candle wax turns liquid, etc.
9. The cup is very hot.
10. The cup is hot, but not as hot as the metal cup.
11. The cup does not get very hot.
12. Your hair stands up.
13. The egg is gooey; has a strong smell.
14. The arms seem to lift without effort.
15. The celery gets red stripes.
16. You feel a rhythmic beating in the neck.
17. A greasy streak is left.
18. The salt and sugar dissolve; the flour, cinnamon, and pepper float on the water and do not mix in well.

pages 42–43

Answers may vary on 1–7, 11–13.

1. elements or radioactive elements
2. mollusks, animals, or invertebrates, or sea animals
3. space objects
4. units of measurement
5. elements or gemstones
6. bones
7. life processes or plant processes
8. water, copper, human body, zinc
9. ant, lobster, frog, gorilla
10. beach, barrier island, spit, tombolo
11–13. animals with segmented bodies, arthropods, animals, invertebrates, animals with many legs
14. water, carbon dioxide, wood, sodium chloride, propane
15. carbon dioxide, wood, propane

pages 44–45

Answers will vary. Check to see that student has written a hypothesis for each example that makes sense, given the observation provided.

page 46

1. miles or kilometers
2. gallons or liters or quarts
3. millimeters
4. gallons, liters, or cubic feet
5. degrees
6. cubic feet, cubic meters
7. hours or minutes
8. inches or centimeters
9. inches or centimeters
10. tons, pounds, or kilograms
11–15. Answers will vary.
16. He measured the weight of each person; measured to find the center of the rope; counted the people; calculated the total weights.

page 47

Answers will vary.

1. Sound gets lower as the glass gets more full.
2. very low sound
3. The tongue senses different tastes on its different parts.
4. the sides

page 48

1. sodium; chlorine
2. sodium; unstable
3. chlorine; stable
4. chlorine; sodium (or from the outer ring of sodium); sodium
5. C

page 49

Answers will vary. Check to see that student has adequately provided explanations and answers for items 1–3.

page 50

Answers will vary.

1. The juice will take longer to freeze than the water.
2. the concentration of the juice solutions
3. the amount of liquid in each solution (or the concentration of juice); the water is a controlled variable also.
4. cups, measuring spoons
5. measuring amounts of water and juice, timing the freezing, counting the cups

page 51

Answers will vary. Check student plans to see that each section is adequately and sensibly completed.

page 52

Answers will vary.

1. correct
2. Use only special lab equipment. Do not use kitchen utensils.
3. correct
4. Always slant tubes away to keep dangerous fumes away from you
5. correct
6. Never eat from lab containers.
7. Never inhale any chemicals.
8. Do not taste any substances in the lab.
9. Wash any spills off immediately.
10. correct
11. Do not wear baggy sleeves or loose clothing.
12. correct
13. If your clothes catch on fire, do not run. OR
If your clothes catch on fire, wrap yourself in a rug or safety blanket.
14. correct
15. Report ALL injuries or accidents
16. Do not dispose of chemicals and lab materials in the sink.